Dear Reader:

You've picked up this book because you are infertile or know someone who is infertile. As an infertility counselor, and a former infertility patient, I have the privilege of discussing, with thoughtful people like you, the fears, sadness, bewilderment, and so many other feelings, that I also have experienced. I have watched couples work through the myriad emotions and ultimately discover the joys of parenthood or, if they choose, resolve their sorrow by making a child-free, not child-less choice.

In this book I want to talk to you in much the same way that I discuss the many issues confronting those who seek my counsel. Although we are not meeting in person, I'd like to help you become your own best counselor; to help you, your mate, your family, or your dearest friends better understand what you are going through, so they can help, too.

The questions presented here are the ones I hear most often from people with impaired fertility. I hope you will find the answers to your questions among them and also take comfort in the words and experiences of others who have traveled the same road you find yourself on now. While it is not a journey we would choose to make, there are many choices of destinations. Remember, you do not have to make it alone.

Sincerely,

Joyce Surkamp Friedeman PhD

ACKNOWLEDGMENTS

First and foremost, I want to thank my husband, Elliott, for his unwavering support and encouragement, and my children for their patience. Second, I wish to express appreciation to my friends and colleagues, including the dedicated people at the Fertility Programs where I consult. Next, I thank the members of RESOLVE, Inc., as well as the researchers and writers in the field of infertility who have provided us with knowledge, perspective and treatment options.

Last and certainly not least, I want to express my gratitude to the persons whose stories I tell in this book, and all of the other infertile clients I have counseled, because they teach me how to better understand their pain, as well as my own, while traveling this road beset with grief but then with joy; frustration, but then resolve. In a spiritual sense, they continually remind me that love for another person, especially a child, and the desire to nurture gives meaning to life, as there is no greater treasure, just as there is no greater loss. My hope is that the words in this book will bring comfort to those who are grieving reproductive loss, as well as encourage them to find empathic people in their lives who will give them the gifts of understanding and acceptance. In most situations, just listening is enough.

Dedicated to
my family
and
to those who have lost children
and dream children.

ON INFERTILITY
Anonymous

It's not fatal,
 but it kills your dreams.

It's not handicapping
 but it cripples you every month.

It's not disfiguring
 but it scars you forever.

It's not fracturing
 but it's breaking your heart.

Introduction

As a professional clinical counselor, nurse, and psychosocial consultant, I have definite beliefs about how people should be counseled when they come to me for help.

The overall goal of psychotherapy, in my opinion, is to help grieving and anxious persons become capable of counseling themselves with the aid of empathic people in their everyday lives. This goal becomes a reality if the clients

1) feel understood

2) trust that my words and actions are intended to help them become healthier and further understand themselves

3) feel accepted, not only for the good that they see in themselves, but also, and more important, for the aspects of themselves they perceive as shameful; the anger, the fear, the vulnerability or weakness

4) cherish <u>all</u> parts of their inner and outer selves

My experience has taught me that if we can allow ourselves to "open up" to one person – therapist or friend– and feel the peace that authenticity can bring, then the ability to confide in another will transfer to other trusted people in our surroundings. Confiding means crying as well as talking. We have a full range of emotions; we will feel them, like it or not, and a certain freedom comes from accepting our real selves.

At times I see people who happen to have a biological predisposition, for example, to depression and panic attacks. In these cases, the person needs intense help, perhaps longer or more frequent professional interventions. Most of the time, however, the people who make up the infertile population need to learn that the labile emotions they are feeling are exceedingly common for folks in their shoes, and with a little guidance, those under the burden of infertility will feel better.

Finally, I think it is imperative that your infertility counselor have first hand experience and knowledge with respect to impaired fertility as well as the phase of decision making or treatment you are facing. The grief of this disheartening malady can seldom be fully appreciated by those who have easily been blessed with as many children as they want, sometimes more than they wanted. As mentioned before, the therapist must understand your imbedded pain, because there is no grief like the grief of losing your children.

These are questions that most people with impaired fertility ask. They are probably on your mind, too.

Why do I feel so upset about being infertile?

Why doesn't anyone understand?

How can we cope with the grief?

What is maternal drive? What part is spiritual?

Do men react to infertility differently from women?

Should we join a support group? How do we start our own support group?

What about secondary infertility? Why do I want another child?

How would we know if we need extra help? What can a professional do for us?

What are the alternatives? When should we examine them? Can we speed up the process?

Although throughout this book I use personal pronouns such as *ours* and *mine,* and because I am a woman, the reader might mistakenly assume that this book was written expressly for women. Please understand that the man's pain in this experience weighs heavily in the impaired fertility equation. As I explain in the *Male's Perspective* section, I have learned that the suffering that men endure, especially if they have lost their reproductive right to rear their genetic children, can be a lifelong trauma. Some men have an extraordinary talent for nurturing children. These men suffer the most, along with their wives, when they, too, must live with continually negative pregnancy tests, in vitro fertilization failures and miscarriages. Have no doubts about it, these men are grieving. Maybe no one will ever know to what depth their sorrow runs. I have done my best to represent the male's viewpoint, but I'm sure what I have written falls short of the whole picture. I welcome your suggestions.

I have tried to make this book as easy to read as possible. Read through it. Pick it up again, from time to time, when you need it. Please put your thoughts in the spaces provided. You may at some point wish to share them with others when you are ready. This is <u>your</u> book. I will give you a helping hand, so you can become your own best counselor.

Note: The stories and quotes I share in this book are all real ones. I have changed names to protect privacy.

HEARTS BREAK AND DREAMS SOAR

WHY DO I FEEL SO UPSET ABOUT BEING INFERTILE?

Understand the magnitude of your loss.

The loss of a child is the greatest loss.

It's natural that you feel upset. Most people do. You are mourning the death of your dream children. This is a tremendous loss, unlike any other. Like Barbara said at a support group meeting, "I know this sounds selfish and stupid, but every time someone else announces that she is pregnant, I feel that she got the baby that was meant for me, and I feel hopeless and jealous. I wish I didn't feel this way. I'm so ashamed."

Just to document the tremendous psychosocial effect of infertility, I asked people who were about to start infertility support groups to complete an infertility inventory regarding their degree of discomfort in the areas of self-esteem, sexuality, self-image, body image, and competence. The scores reflected that all group members reported that infertility had seriously disturbed all or most of these aspects of their lives.

1

The nature of grief

What you are feeling, in large part, is a grief reaction, a universal set of responses that affects your entire being. Those who have experienced grief will tell you that a sudden, personal loss will assault your entire being, stop your world. When you suffer the death of a loved one, you are stricken with grief. This bereavement is no stranger to many of us. In extreme cases we find it difficult to sleep, eat, and have interest in activities we once enjoyed, including sexual expression. There is a sense that we are merely "going through the motions" of life, feeling as though we are empty or "just a shell."

Grief is a time-consuming process; we can't get over it until we get through it. During the critical six weeks or so after the loss, we feel the sorrow most intensely; thereafter, the feelings are mellowed by support from others and by the passage of time. On certain significant dates, relevant to the life of the one we have lost, we'll feel the grief again more intensely. One particularly grievous time is the one year anniversary of the loss and subsequent yearly anniversaries.

During a recent interview, a tearful woman suddenly realized why she dreads autumn. Her sister drowned two years ago in early September, and her dad died four years ago in October. To compound her grief, she had just been told that the baby boy she joyfully carried for five months no longer had a heartbeat. Her miscarriage was felt as deeply as losing a child who was born. Obviously she was suffering not only from her baby's death but also from the accumulated grief of the other losses, almost as though they were a flashback.

Connie's miscarriages

Connie, a superbly competent woman and former client of mine who suffered two miscarriages, endured profound emotional pain followed by depression and anxiety. "Why do people trivialize infertility? They don't trivialize cancer!" In order to cope with her desperation she wrote a thesis on the subject of miscarriage. Even the term mis-carriage, she thought, is disparaging to the carrier, the gestating mom, i.e., she "missed" the baby, as if she missed questions on a test and failed. Connie also examined the expression, "I lost the baby." Most would agree it is shameful to lose something important. "It's not that I left him on the bus!" Why did you lose it? Weren't you careful? Didn't it mean enough to you? Not surprisingly, many women feel ashamed about having a miscarriage, followed, of course, by hurt, anger, guilt, and so on.

Connie, with time and a supportive husband, has resolved most of her grief, coped with her depression and anxiety, and will pursue a few more Pergonal cycles in which the doctor will inseminate her husband's sperm into her uterus. If she isn't pregnant after those cycles, they will try in vitro fertilization. She and her husband hold great hope for this procedure, yet they know they have about a 15%-30% chance of becoming pregnant and delivering a healthy baby. In the back of their minds, however, they know they may have to choose to adopt a child or decide to be child-free. They know they have control of at least those decisions.

Yvonne's tubal pregnancies

In the case of tubal pregnancies, the mortification that infertile women feel is even more searing. Yvonne, who had an ectopic pregnancy, cried, "I finally got pregnant – with twins! My babies wanted to be born, but I couldn't grow them in the right place!" Yvonne knew, only too well, that in the aftermath of miscarriage, how the perfunctory comments like "don't worry, you'll get pregnant right away" or "it's a good thing, the baby might have been deformed" do nothing for us but discount our emotional pain, leaving us feeling lonely when we need comforting. Certainly with repeated ectopic pregnancies, miscarriages and stillbirths, the grief becomes a large part of our lives.

After months of expressing her sorrow, Yvonne planted two lilac bushes in her yard and named her baby boys Adam and Patrick. They will always be her first two children. Eventually, Yvonne gave birth to her third baby, who will learn about her brothers who died.

The unique grief suffered by infertile persons is not mollified easily, because commonly the losses continue to happen. Each negative pregnancy test is like a death, the death of that imagined child. You can bond to the developing infant after three weeks, the same way you bond to the baby after nine weeks. So, "she was only pregnant for three weeks" discounts your grief. The anticipation of the birth of a child reaches larger-than-life proportions in the daydreams of its parents, thus beginning the process of attachment. They already have the child in school, in sports, in social activities, etc. So why is it so hard for people to understand that miscarriage can be perceived as a death? Similarly, when embryos are transferred to the uterus in an in vitro fertilization, some of us are closer to pregnancy than we ever were, and the loss of the embryos feels like the loss of children whom we have already named and sent to college.

For these reasons, the tumultuous circumstances of infertility create an unexpected and often shattering situational crisis. We have an easier time dealing with the maturational crises of life. We are prepared, more or less, to lose our parents, maybe even our siblings or our spouse, but the loss of our children is an unexpected

5

tragedy. This crisis state is a level of consciousness with heightened fear, vulnerability and other volatile emotions. With infertility, the temporary aspect of the crisis is questionable, as the condition may become chronic. Soldiers home from a war may suffer Post Traumatic Stress Disorder (PTSD), a psychological condition in which they relive the stunning loss of a compatriot, have nightmares about seeing civilians shot. The community offers sympathy and understanding to these veterans, and well it should.

Rarely, however do people not afflicted with infertility understand the heartache of a mom like Linda, continually confronted with diaper commercials on TV, and mothers showing off their precious babies at church. All the while, Linda carries in her womb her infant girl who died last week. The doctors want Linda to wait for nature to take its course, to wait until the uterus pushes out the lifeless form in what is called a *spontaneous abortion*. <u>How do we measure emotional pain</u>? Who is suffering more?

> *Grieving is as natural as*
> *crying when you are hurt,*
> *sleeping when you are tired,*
> *eating when you are hungry,*
> *or sneezing when your nose itches.*
> *It is nature's way of healing a*
> *broken heart.*
>
> *Don't Take My Grief Away*
> Doug Manning

Why Are Holidays So Hard?

They are difficult for virtually everyone.

Did you know that holidays are documented to be emotionally difficult for virtually everyone? Of all the Christian holidays, Christmas tops the list for generating stress, next is Thanksgiving, then individual differences come into play.

What do we traditionally think of when we fantasize about Christmas: Santa Claus (for children), <u>baby</u> Jesus, *The Christmas Song* "tiny tots with their eyes all aglow", our memories of childhood at Christmas time, (sad and happy), and perhaps how we would be better parents to our children than our parents were to us?

Let's face it, children are the focus of Christmas when we are in the reproductive years. On December 25th we dream of telling our families that we are expecting a baby. How many of us hold that holiday along with New Year's Day the critical time at which we decide if we've succeeded or failed at making a baby? If you don't have the child of your dreams or are not expecting a baby, you are

7

depressed. There is very little yuletide joy. You may feel you are, once again, putting on a merry front, wanting to punch the next person who says, "Oh, you should have children – they're what Christmas is all about" or "Is your Christmas shopping done?" when you wish you could shop for what you really want in your heart, your baby.

This holiday season, as well as the Jewish celebration of the eight nights of Hanukah, illuminate our sorrow and heighten our feelings of isolation. How can we be over-flowing with joy when our children or dream children are dead or dying? Our grief is accentuated not only during the winter holidays but also at any time when we are expected to publicly celebrate. It is best for us at these times of celebration to find our own meaning, start our own private traditions. Remember, this acute grief will not last forever. You will find peace and can resume joy in your life.

The key advice here is not to pretend you are exhila-rated as so many others seem to be. Remain authentic, explain to loved ones what you feel. If you don't have the energy to do that, stay home with your partner or go someplace where you can be yourselves.

WHY DOESN'T ANYONE UNDERSTAND?

Finding empathic support.

"They say I'm making this worse than it is, that I'm bringing it on myself. People can't see how hard this is."

You are right. Typically, fertile people (80% of the population) don't understand, and this lack of empathy intensifies our grief because we wind up feeling alienated. After all, in most cases there is no funeral service, no baby to bury, no friends calling to offer support. We feel we are left alone with our sorrow. We are lucky if we have one or two confidantes with whom we can share our hidden sadness.

As you know, empathic means feeling <u>with</u> you, walking a mile in your shoes. Empathy is not pity or condescension. Empathy implies understanding in the fullest sense of the word. Individuals who have lost parents, siblings, spouses, and of course children, will understand grief but may not see your grief as commensurate to theirs.

9

Insensitive acquaintances said to me, "You just have to accept that God doesn't want you to have everything in life that you think you want." We can educate them, tell them we have lost children, which in no way can be compared to the loss of material assets. A neighbor said exactly that to an infertile colleague. "We all have our crosses to bear, my plans for a new house fell through, Jimmy did not get into the college he wanted" and so on. Incredible as it may seem, people who have no concept of the devastation of infertility equate losing a pregnancy with missing a vacation or losing a job. Unfortunately, trying to communicate with people like this is futile. There are sensitive listeners out there; with persistence you will find them.

Thus, we need to realize the enormity of our loss, find empathic support, and a partner in grief is paramount. If we frame our picture of ourselves as persevering in spite of bereavement, we will feel that we deserve to grieve. Even though most people won't understand the depth of your sorrow, you and those closest to you must realize what your losses mean to you.

> *I wonder –*
> > *Does God gossip?*
> > *Does He talk to other folks about me?*
> *If not, why do they think they*
> > *know His way for me?*
> *If He does*
> > *I wish He would quit it.*

> > *Don't Take My Grief Away*
> > Doug Manning

AM I MAKING MYSELF MORE ANXIOUS AND DEPRESSED?

Increased stress is a result, not a cause of infertility.

Experts have shown there is no "infertile personality." For example, back in a 1987 is-

sue of the **Journal of In-vitro Fertilization and Embryo Transfer,** the report of a study showed that 90% of 94 women subjects in infertility treatment reported feeling frustration, depression, hopelessness, and anger. The authors rated the subjects' level of stress as greater than that caused by divorce or death of a close friend or family member. In the same journal, two years later, the researchers found that patients undergoing in vitro fertilization were found to be normal on all psychological parameters, meaning that the women, contrary to some popular myths, were not diagnosed with hysterical neuroses, panic disorder, manic depression, or any other mental illness.

The increased stress that you feel is a result, not a

cause, of your infertility. Frequently, couples worry that their stress at the time of possible conception prevents conception or implantation. We could spend a lot of time analyzing what we were doing wrong during those critical hours or minutes – worrying about our ailing mother, distracted by concerns over financial resources, not thinking positively enough.

Indeed, we all should be in a perfect frame of mind while we are making love or being inseminated, but of course, no one can be perfect. Even our fertile neighbor complains of oceans of stress, even painful intercourse, but she continues to have more children. How is it that abused wives get pregnant? Rape victims sometimes get pregnant; how perfect were their states of mind? Extreme physical and mental stress, however, which may be seen in anorexia or compulsive exercising, may cause ovulation dysfunction and loss of menses.

Assuming we are doing everything we can to be at our optimum level of health and psychological equilibrium, what are some pragmatic ideas to help us cope with our grief?

HOW CAN WE COPE WITH THE GRIEF?

Ten steps to take.

1. Give ourselves permission to grieve.

This may seem obvious to you, but I believe that feeling entitled to grief is one of our most difficult tasks. We have an easier time accepting the feelings in ourselves if others give us acceptance and love in our grief. Grieving carries with it the feelings of anger, fear, and guilt, along with the sorrow. You will be angry, sometimes lashing out at your partner, or you may scream at your doctor or nurse. Your anger is fueled by the imbedded pain.

Lack of recognition of the pain by you and your partner will result in deeper hurt and more anger as the losses leave you feeling hopeless and helpless. Pat Johnston, in **Taking Charge of Infertility**, helps us gain perspective by enumerating these losses or potential losses:

1. Control over many aspects of life

2. Individual genetic continuity linking past and future

3. The joint conception of a child with one's life partner

4. The physical satisfactions of pregnancy and birth

5. The emotional gratification of pregnancy and birth

6. The opportunity to parent

Our acceptance of the losses and the secondary loss of self-worth will help assuage our guilt and soothe our pain, as we say to ourselves, "It's okay to feel this bad. I'm normal, but I need extra caring every day from loved ones." Our task (as though we need another one!) is to teach those we care about to understand the breadth of our losses.

People will say to you, "You're dwelling too much on this, you should try again right away or adopt a child." They don't get it. If they had lost a child they'd know you can't replace one person with another. What if their spouse died? Would you be asking them to date after two weeks? Would you say, "Just get another husband?" Please educate people who make these comments, help them understand that grief, over time, is necessary for healing the wounds.

Another way of giving ourselves permission to grieve is to avoid situations where we would feel terribly sad. Some of us hate going to hospitals to see new babies, or attending baptisms and Mother's Day celebrations. Let's honor these valid limitations. Why force ourselves to feel worse? This is a phase in our lives, it won't last forever. Would we expect a Vietnam soldier to see a movie about front line combat and murdered children a few months after he was discharged?

Just today, Sally, in the throes of grief after her baby girl died minutes after delivery, asked me how to deal with her best friend who is one month pregnant. Sally tearfully described how she needed support from her long time ally but feared the pregnancy would interfere with her rapport. I advised Sally to speak daily on the phone to her friend to avoid the onslaught of more painful feelings. Then, after the baby is born, my client can meet the baby, in private, when she is emotionally ready.

2. Give expression to our feelings and thoughts.

We have voices for a reason. The best thing we can do for our mental health is to express what we think and feel to people who have a non-judgmental ear. Our anger, grief, and fear is normal.

When we express these feelings by writing, drawing, dancing, playing music, etc., we are moving through the grief from the cumulative losses we have sustained thus far.

Our tears tell the truth – let them flow freely. Take time to be real with supportive friends or family about your worries. My advice to those in grief is <u>if you can't be real, don't be there</u>. Tears and feelings are messy and can leave you feeling disheveled. But like the story of the Velveteen Rabbit, being real will bring more true friendship with others who care than the velvet facade of perfectionism. Look how these women did it.

Viola

Viola, an accomplished artist, refocused her career by painting magnificent abstracts of infertility, sharing her feelings of frustration, barrenness, and hope in huge, striking images. Her stunning work was shown in some major galleries. She began feeling as though people could understand and appreciate her work. After a few years, Viola and her husband adopted a red-haired baby girl who is the "love of my life", according to Viola. She continues to paint about infertility because she wants others to appreciate their struggle.

Lorri

Lorri started her own children's band and conducted music therapy with abused children to express the gamut of her feelings about her reproductive losses. Her efforts have made it possible for underprivileged children with few resources to become rather accomplished musicians, poised in the spotlight. The children are blossoming with pride and so is Lorri. Their stamina is giving her strength in her quest for a child of her own.

Janice

Let me tell the story of Janice, a brave woman who tried to have children for six years while her eight brothers and sisters produced babies, even while using contraception. The children and grandchildren were the focus of her extended family, especially of Janice's own parents. Suffering two miscarriages in seven years, then losing a third pregnancy after 22 weeks, Janice recognized that she was carrying her emotional pain with only her husband and a few friends to help her.

Instead of becoming bitter toward her inattentive family, she wrote them a poignant letter describing how she had been grieving silently for seven years and how now she was asking for their understanding and support. The letter was well received. Janice welcomed phone calls and greeting cards from every member of her family. She was glad she had shared her distress and felt enormous acceptance. Janice and her family appropriately cried together. The family's open communication has enhanced their relationship with Janice and her husband, as well as with other extended family members.

One other way Janice learned to cope with her grief was to find a kitten that she and her husband could nurture. "Actually, it was my husband's idea, and now both of us love that silly cat." Some people discount the value of  pets in our lives, but, in my experience, the bonding that can occur with an animal is therapeutic. Pets, in addition, can promote a sense of humor in us in an otherwise somber day.

Ronnie

Ronnie came to see me for the express purpose of talking about a three year history of infertility, but quickly her words turned to the story of her mother's death. Ronnie witnessed her mother's death from metastatic cancer six months previously. Her mother died in a hospital bed in Ronnie's living room. Weeping, Ronnie recalled the numerous nursing care tasks she performed lovingly for her mom, not an easy job for an accountant. Over a period of four weeks, she described in minute detail the mental pictures that were still fresh in her mind. As she cried, she realized she had not told her story to anyone, not even her husband, because the content was overwhelming to her. How could she burden her husband with her grief?

I became Ronnie's partner in grief as I walked with her through the thirty-two days of her mother's dignified death. At the close of therapy, Ronnie reported the immense satisfaction of having traveled that sorrowful road once more, this time being able to feel all of her emotions instead of being stoic. Three months later, Ronnie became pregnant and now has two healthy children. The pregnancy probably has nothing to do with the counseling, but Ronnie believed she had to work through that grief before she could allow herself to become pregnant. She said that even if she hadn't become pregnant, she would have felt more freedom in seeking the right reproductive choice for herself and her husband.

Ronnie had a <u>partner in grief</u> who happened to be me. Anyone who has the time, interest, and can lend an empathic ear when we need to express our sorrow can be our partner in grief. If we can find more than one grief partner we are even more fortunate, especially at those times when we feel we need to attend a function but can't face the experience alone. When our partner in grief accompanies us, we can be more at peace because the partner understands what we are going through and serves as a buffer between us and the non-supportive, or at least unconcerned, public.

3. Do something tangible to validate and memorialize our losses.

This idea may sound strange to us at first, but when we think of the ritual that encircles the bereaved when a loved one has died, the cards, flowers, visitation, funeral, prayers at the gravesite, weeks of food delivered to the door, and so forth, we understand that all of this supportive structure is meant to soothe the grief and show the bereaved that they are not alone in their sorrow. We who have suffered infertility losses rarely get an empathic word, much less a show of hearty support.

Nobody knows, nobody cares, is our shell-shocked reaction, but with a proactive stance, we can show in a concrete way that what we've been through really does matter. In fact, I attended an inspiring memorial service for a couple who survived three miscarriages. Their families and friends gathered at their home. A priest read prayers, others gave testimony to the courage of the devoted couple. We sang lyrics some of us had composed for the occasion, then stayed to eat and offer condolence.

In remembrance, others have planted trees, hung plaques on their mantles, created scrapbooks with pictures of stillborn babies or of their ultrasounds and pre-embryos or cards and letters, written books, music and created other works of art. With <u>something to hold</u>, to cherish, we remind ourselves that these dream children are remembered in our homes and gardens as well as in our hearts. We do have something to show for it.

4. Refuse to blame ourselves, our spouses, or God.

Do you secretly believe that it is your fault that you can't have a baby? You don't know exactly what you did that was wrong, but you have prodigious ideas, such as the time you had unprotected intercourse at age 18, or the contribution you made to Planned Parenthood, or even the year you decided to boycott Sunday religious services because there were so many babies. Maybe if your attitude were more optimistic? Will God let you have a baby if you put in more volunteer hours at the Senior Center? These thoughts are abundant in the clients that I counsel. We reproach ourselves for having these ideas, but suffer all the more because, in private moments, they haunt us.

If you believe in God, or a higher power, I hope this belief brings positive energy to you in times of sorrow. Religious values are meant to support us, to forgive and provide strength. In his book, **When Bad Things Happen to Good People,** Harold Kushner, who lost a son to progeria, emphasizes the profound loss of the infertile couple and how useless it is to blame ourselves. In a similar vein, **Don't Take My Grief Away** was written by a protestant minister to help people understand the process and tenacity of grief, and most essentially that you can't effectively put grief on a shelf or hurry to get through it. Acquaintances, though well intentioned, will want to rush you to get over your bereavement, but the grieving cannot be pushed away. **And Hannah Wept** is a rabbi's personal look at the nadir a couple, like he and his wife felt, when they could not bear children, yet how they found comfort in a higher power and in empathic company.

Religious beliefs that God is accepting and forgiving can bring solace to the soul. Most organized religions, have a degree of tolerance and some skepticism about infertility treatment, depending on how strictly a certain community of people follow a doctrine. Catholic clients I have met commonly seek counsel from their parish priests over issues such as intra-uterine insemination. The reform rabbis look more favorably upon infertility treatments than the orthodox rabbis. I advise people to follow their conscience and have a dialogue with a member of their clergy whom they trust.

5. Be especially caring toward ourselves and our partner, and protective of our self-esteem.

As you may have guessed, caring for ourselves is another perplexing job for many of us. Our stress levels are higher than usual because of our normal anxiety about each step of our treatment. Both of you may be more irritable, but keep in mind that this heightened emotional vulnerability is temporary. Wives commonly are more intense and tearful than husbands regarding infertility treatment. Help your partners understand your stress and encourage them to talk about theirs.

I shall mention the notion of journaling more than once. Keep a family or individual journal of your thoughts and feelings. This simple booklet may become one of your most treasured mementos. An ingenious couple I know began their journal ten years ago and now, every day, they, as well as their son, write and draw in the journal, which now has five volumes. It has become their *family history.* Focusing on yourselves long enough to write your thoughts and feelings in a special place is an especially effective way of caring for yourselves and building self-esteem.

The use of simple, comforting remedies like touching, back rubs, and so on, are crucial to improved self-esteem. Treat yourselves to time spent together to replenish your good feelings. Making love, of course, without the performance anxiety of sex on demand at a prescribed time, is healing and alleged to release important endorphins. All of these measures can add a little more pleasure to your lives that now may feel nearly void of enjoyment. In a subsequent section on nurturing your relationship, I will present other ideas about keeping your marriage alive and well during infertility.

In keeping with the mind–body connection, even though you may not be thinking about taking care of your body at this time, please avoid tobacco, as it depletes our bodies of nutrients and hampers our circulatory system. Reduce alcohol and caffeine consumption, drink at least 8 glasses of liquid a day and eat a healthful diet. During the winter solstice, enjoy sunlight as much as possible to help avert Seasonal Affective Disorder. Finally do something physically active every day even if it's a walk around the block.

6. Ask for what we need to avoid the complications of co-dependent behavior.

Lisa

Just yesterday I met with a personable and articulate woman, Lisa, who wondered why she was devastated after six failed cycles. We discussed the reasons that her feelings are pretty much universal. There is an aspect to her grief, though, which often goes unnoticed. She is one of the people, by admission, who takes care of everyone and everything else first before she takes care of herself. Granted, there are a lot of us out there; it must be part of how a woman learns. But this way of life, nice as it may seem, gets us in trouble on occasions when we need more time and nurturing for ourselves and can't seem to find it.

Naturally, Lisa's family and friends are accustomed to her giving and giving. If she hadn't experienced this crisis of infertility, she may have continued her apparently selfless behavior without ever thinking about it. But when she realized that she needed support, attention, and love, others were not rallying to her side. They didn't notice. They couldn't imagine something could be wrong with her. She had always handled everything, it was hardly in their repertoires to offer support to Lisa. Doing everything for everybody is, of course, an exaggeration, but some women do come close to this way of maintaining relationships.

You know the term *co-dependency*, which is a way of relating that springs from shame. Lisa unwittingly tried to maintain control over her life and sometimes over others' lives by doing too much for them. She allowed her family to depend too much on her, and refused to admit to her own needs for attention and support. Not that every giving person is co-dependent, but, in the extreme, this behavior leads to dysfunctional, non-supportive relationships.

In other words, if you are like Lisa, you acquire most of your needs for nurturing by nurturing someone else. A consequence of this cycle, however, is that you, the "nice" woman or man, continue to feel needy inside. Conversely, the significant others feel irritated because, if you continually do everything for them, they perceive that you see them as incompetent. Both of you wind up feeling helpless, scared, and angry. Another major consequence of this behavior is that you don't have the opportunity to learn to ask for help or take a dependent role. Both independent and dependent behaviors are healthy. The key is to balance these roles in a context of interdependency.

The solution, easier to say than do, is to ask, in a straightforward way, for what we want. Naturally, our request will be directed toward the person whose attention we seek. With this approach, your mate can help or refuse to help, but at least you've been honest and know where he stands, and he, also, has been authentic. Obviously, we can't control how others are going to respond to us or feel about us. We can only control our own responses, and perhaps we have some trouble doing that. Facing the fact that we are only human is difficult at best.

To further illustrate this point, some of us (we don't see it, but others do) wear a "sign" that says, "I can take care of myself and I can take care of you" but on the back side of the sign it says, "I really won't take care of myself." At the other end of the spectrum, some people wear one saying, "I can't take care of myself and I can't take care of you."

These are extremes, and you can conjure up all of the in-between messages the signs can broadcast. If you wear the first sign, you will have more difficulty getting the emotional support you need from others. If you wear the second sign, you may receive pity. Ideally, your sign would read, "Most of the time I can take care of myself, but when I can't, I will ask you to help me through the rough spots" and "I'd like to be able to take care of you sometimes, if you want or ask me to help." Lisa could not find support until she stopped wearing the first sign and began admitting that she, too, needed attention.

Along these lines, I'll offer a metaphor that has helped some of my clients and myself visualize our predicament when it comes to giving versus taking, or putting out energy versus pulling in strength. Let's use the concept of our *vessel* (our soul, spirit) being full versus empty. In our vessel is a core concept of self which gives our vessel definition and form. We hope this intrinsic self-image is fairly positive and enduring. When people show us love and respect, we feel more valued, our vessel is full. When

27

we are plunged into grief by an unexpected loss, we lose sight of our healthy self. We begin to blame ourselves as our self-esteem gets muddied. Since we have long forgotten how to ask for, or felt we needed, the positive affirmation we social beings need, our vessel gradually loses its essence.

At that juncture, if we continue to nurture others, throw baby showers and distribute tickets at the church's family picnic, our vessel disintegrates. We don't have enough positive feedback from others, or even self-love, to give it shape. I use this metaphor with clients who overextend themselves to help them hold on to the axiom that we cannot continue to give if we have nothing left to give. We must take the time to fill the vessel with nurturing goods, including time for ourselves to talk, walk, meditate, write, get a massage or yoga lesson, even to nap. These are a few ways of showing others, not to mention ourselves, what we need. You can discover even better ways.

7. Be prepared for insensitive remarks by others.

You've been made very aware by now that a large proportion of infertile people avoid social situations where people may ask embarrassing questions or make rude comments. Sadly, these humiliating experiences keep us from attending functions we formerly enjoyed. Not long ago at a RESOLVE meeting, I was asked to give a talk on how we can respond to inane comments about our impaired fertility and reproductive losses. Together we listed about 50 statements that generated stress within us. A few examples: *I think you're smart not wanting kids. Wow, with two incomes and no kids, you've got money to throw away. You want kids? You can have three of mine! You shouldn't wait too long to have children, your biological clock is ticking. Why don't you just adopt? Don't you think some people take this infertility stuff too seriously? At least you didn't know the baby. You should have quit work. You should have kept working so you couldn't worry as much. I told you, you were too stressed out. Some things in this world you just can't have. Some people weren't meant to be parents.* I'm sure you could add 20 more.

Can you imagine walking into a party having rehearsed honest, self-confident replies or just a clever quip for every one of those all too common remarks? Let's delineate several categories of responses. The first I call the **educational approach,** that is, tell the questioner more than she would ever want to know about infertility diagnoses, and don't fail to decipher your L.H. surge. She can stand in awe of your medical acumen and quickly will want to change the topic to retirement plans.

A second response, called **turnabout is fair play,** is a comeback for the man who offers you his children. You might offer your sympathy that he must have trouble setting limits on his children, or you could politely suggest parenting classes. For the lady who thinks you take infertility too seriously, you could ask her how seriously she takes a fever of 103 degrees in her 6 month old.

A third approach we may take is the **pick a word** technique, that is, we focus on a term the other person uses and question him about that term. An example would be, "What do you mean by 'obsessed' about having a baby...is that like being obsessed with your job...where does healthy concern become pathological obsession...?"

The epitome of conversation stoppers, the **meant to be** observer, who can rationalize everything with, "there is a good reason for that," ask how she decides what is meant to be and how is it that some people are meant to be retarded or even why is it that she was meant to be a parent? I'm sure she could also divulge some very interesting theories about who is destined to be the judge of what is meant to be and for whom.

A fourth response is the **find an excuse** technique, which is necessary for invitations to baby naming ceremonies and all of those other activities that you know from experience will compound your feelings of loss. A helpful term is conflict, as in, "I'm sorry, I have a conflict on that date."

The last approach I'll address here is the **blame your doctor** strategy. "My doctor says I can't attend functions like that until my treatment is over," which your doctor or counselor is sure to corroborate. A corollary of blame your doctor is to **blame the medicine.** You are in the third week of a Pergonal cycle and your emotions change with mercurial speed, especially from sadness to irritability and back to sadness. You say to your colleagues at the board meeting, "Please don't be alarmed if I start crying, some medicine I take makes me cry for no reason."

Wouldn't it be interesting to put together a pamphlet listing all the apropos responses we can think of to these naive but hurtful comments? We don't have to be sarcastic. We can soften our approach when we wish, if the person is truly concerned, but I want to emphasize that we do have many empowering replies in our repertoire, if only we think a moment or two about how we'd like to respond. You are entitled to stand up for yourself.

You'll recognize that the thrust of some of these suggestions have an assertive tone, as if you are implying "I'm not going to sit here and let you partronize me." You may feel uncomfortable sounding so direct. Obviously, if you're not comfortable with some of these approaches, use the ones which won't be construed as caustic. Remember, though, anger is a substantial part of grief. You have anger inside of you, we all do. You will need to accept this part of yourself and realize you have a right to express assertive opinions without hurting anyone else.

A massage therapist and friend suggests that we choose among these empowering responses which enhance our self concepts:

1. "I want to and I will." (a straightforward option)

2. "I want to but I won't." (such as start smoking again)

3. "I don't want to but I will." (go to the supermaket)

4. "I don't want to and I won't." (attend that baptism)

5. "I'll wait awhile to make a decision." (refusing to be put on the spot for a quick answer)

An example of a dis-empowering option is "I don't want to but I should/or I have to." (allowing the opinion of others to direct our lives)

It is so easy to feel out of control as an infertile person. Regaining control by using the five options will increase your confidence around people. You'll know you can stand your ground.

8. Dredge up some fun in your life. Use humor judiciously.

If I asked, "What do you do for fun?" are you like most infertility patients who look at me, perplexed, and say something like, "What fun?" Then I ask, "What did you do for fun before infertility?" This question helps couples gain some perspective, remembering there was a time when they did act silly and laugh a lot. Make a list of what you enjoyed before infertility. See if you can enjoy one or two of those activities now.

Activities We Enjoy

_____

_____

_____

_____

_____

_____

_____

_____

_____

_____

_____

_____

When we are in the middle of grief and torpor, leisure isn't in our vocabulary. But, as mentioned before, if we can take a short break in treatment, especially after a stunning loss, we open the door just a crack to allow a bit of pleasure to sneak in.

With vacations, not necessarily the two week kind (how about the two day break?), we may gain a fresher outlook on our lives, and perhaps recognize some of the absurdities of our circumstances. Sometimes the outrageous can be funny. I wish I had logged all the quips that brought comic relief to our support groups. From crazy stories about rectal thermometers to dunking husbands in tubs of ice cubes to improve their sperm counts, something always brought a belly laugh. What about the athlete who fainted the first time he had to give his wife a Pergonal injection? And the time Susan, an executive traveling on business, felt like an idiot asking the hotel registrar if there was anyone there who could give her a shot?

Hilarity that springs from group discussions when couples divulge the various sexual positions they are urged to use is momentous. To ensure conception, we listen to stories about standing on our heads, throwing away our husbands' jockey shorts, and so on. I remember waiting in stirrups on an exam table for an endometrial biopsy when the fire alarm sounded and the physician and nurse left the room with the door open. I find it slightly humorous that the pregnancy test was the only test I ever failed, and did so repeatedly.

The men in the groups commiserated for hours about their terror in the specimen collection rooms, the poor quality videotapes, the girlie magazines, the acoustics of the room and wondering if staff members could hear them. They recounted the embarrassment of walking out with the semen, and how to phrase the statement about what they were giving the nurse in that little plastic container.

Laughter really is good medicine, but we don't need the hostile humor that implies we don't know how to perform intercourse. On one memorable occasion, a physician who was treating us for infertility jokingly described in detail how each of his seven children was conceived. The youngest child was procreated "after I came home from a hunting trip...the wife was asleep, but it worked anyway." I guess his intent was to entertain me, but a few weeks later, he allowed me to present a seminar in his office to him and his staff on how to be sensitive to infertile patients. That was years ago, today reproductive endocrinologists are very savvy to the emotional discomfort of infertility treatment. Many fertility offices recommend or provide counseling as a matter of routine. Erma Bombeck struck a funny cord when she stated, "Infertile people get about as much sympathy as an 80 lb. woman at a Weight Watchers meeting." With all of the emphasis these days on having a perfect and fit physique, how many infertile people would trade someone with a ten pound weight problem for her fertility?

9. Read what we can to gain knowledge and reassurance.

In addition to the books already mentioned, articles proliferate in the professional and lay press to assist you with your journey to resolution, helping to pave the arduous road to parenthood. Our friends in RESOLVE, Inc., at the local, state, and national level, print up-to-the-minute annotated bibliographies of relevant books. You may also send for information sheets on a particular subject. The state and national RESOLVE newsletters not only contain state of the art information, but include personal stories, poetry, and humor by compatriots who are in the same boat as you. We, in addition, can correspond with others who present their stories in the letters to the editor.

Perspectives Press offers numerous excellent books and pamphlets. Your doctors' offices, especially the fertility centers can recommend other resources. At the end of this booklet, you'll find an abbreviated list of my favorites. I hope some of them will help you.

10. Do our best to take charge of our lives as much as possible.

Be stingy with your personal time. Demands from friends and family, as well as household chores, can wait. Instead, make specific *together plans* with your partner during the days before and after the pregnancy test, that is, plan activities which, in the past, have brought you some pleasure or comfort.

One couple I know takes walks at a nature preserve in the evening when small children are in bed, another dines late at a favorite restaurant, then views an art film. In this way, instead of focusing entirely on the results of the pregnancy test, you can remember that you'll be spending time together in a special place. That time together gives you the opportunity to process the day's events and express your feelings and thoughts about how you perceived those events. These plans are best implemented if actually marked on your calendar the same way you mark all the other events you do for others. Your self-support plans are more important at this time in your

TAKE CHARGE CALENDAR

life than most of the other dates already scheduled.

During the weeks of treatment, patients often feel as though other people are controlling their lives with blood tests, shots, sonograms, prescribed activity and so on. It is important for you to feel that you are running your own life. Talk to your doctors and nurses about suggestions you may have to regain some control. For example, some patients, when the time comes for hearing results of the pregnancy test, find that they are more comfortable calling the Fertility Center at an agreed upon time, rather than waiting on pins and needles all afternoon for that critical phone call.

Take charge by making plans, but also by taking breaks. I can't count the number of times desperate couples have said to me, "I know we need a break, but we're afraid to lose time – it could happen next month." My advice is to take all the breaks you need, and if you're not sure you need it, err on the side of rest. Our psychosocial equilibrium cannot maintain itself on chronic stress. If you feel overwhelmed, the healthy choice is a respite from treatment.

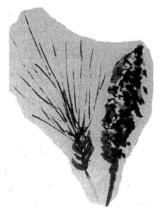

Our Thoughts and Feelings...

WHAT IS MATERNAL DRIVE? WHAT PART IS SPIRITUAL?

An instinct as old as time.

We in the civilized nations are so caught up in logical solutions, technology and materialism that we often dismiss the earthy concept of maternal drive. Wouldn't you predict that even in the twenty first century, little girls will play with dolls and plan to be mommies?

Sarah

Sarah, a successful architect, stopped contraceptives three years ago. Then she took a year off to focus on having a baby. "When I was six years old, I told my dad that I had two babies in my tummy that were waiting to be born. I even knew their names." After three years of disappointments, she says, "My maternal drive is thwarted, I am drowning in sadness. The memory of my dreams as a six year old wanting to be a mommy more than anything are still with me. I've become obsessed."

A spiritual woman, Sarah wrote poetry to express her imbedded emotional pain. Her scientific mind could not reconcile her irrefutable need for a child. Her husband reassured her that he could be happy for the rest of his life with her, with or without children. Still desperate for a baby, Sarah is scheduled for a second in vitro fertilization and has sought a lawyer's advice on independent adoption.

We wonder how much of the maternal drive is from our animal nature and how much interplays with our spiritual nature. Dr. Clarissa Pinkola Estes writes about women's "instinctual nature" in her best-seller, **Women Who Run With Wolves.** The trouble is, fertility doctors, mostly men, can certainly understand the reasons for wanting a family, but they are frequently puzzled by a woman who would risk her career, her emotional stability, and even her marriage to have and rear a child. I tell husbands, who are dismayed with their wives' never-ending pursuit of a baby, that maternal drive is "bigger than all of us." He often says, "Am I not enough for her? She wants a child more than she wants me!" Actually, I believe, in humans, that a woman's maternal drive is propelled by her love of a mate.

So, what is spiritual about the maternal drive? I remember thinking, "If God, or nature, put this extraordinary need for children in me, how am I supposed to forget it and go on with my life?" I prayed that God would take away the drive so my life wouldn't be so conflictive. This is a spiritual dilemma that many of us have had to examine in our own way.

Jessica

Jessica, now premenopausal, and her husband had endured ten years of infertility, four high tech procedures, and even used a donor egg. She once said to me, "I don't know if I can take the disapproval anymore...my husband is so loving and my family so supportive, but they think I've done this long enough. They don't understand my persistence." Then she divulged that she had become so depressed that she could not function in her law practice and spent too many days in bed. Jessica needed reassurance that many other women I meet have the same feelings.

Women like Jessica have come to a point where their families are insisting that they stop. Her reproductive endocrinologist even encouraged her not to go on. "But I know I have the inner strength to continue. I've made prudent choices all of my life, I don't believe I'm jeopardizing my health, so why can't they stick with me?"

Jessica impressed me with her competence. I felt she could pursue another in vitro fertilization attempt if her family and doctor would continue to support her. We discussed ways to help her family see her perspective. Jessica reminds me of so many of us who say, "I have worked hard all my life toward goals I think are important, I proved to myself I can do virtually anything I want to do, but this very fundamental need to have children goes unfulfilled." This realization is incredulous because, as I've said before, it is so totally unexpected. Jessica finally got pregnant from a frozen embryo transfer and is now the happy mother of twins.

As an aside, I also believe from experience in my counseling as well as in friendships that women, as part of their instinctual selves, know the number of children they want to have. I call this the *Maternal Quota*. My neighbor, for example, had four beautiful children, but at age 43 yearned for one more. She questioned her sanity, so did her husband, but she knew this need was undeniable. Their fifth child, Missy, is a born leader and an outstanding dancer. I have yet to speak with a woman who, if she wants children, does not know how many children she hopes for. This is not to say, of course, that all women and men, for that matter, want to have offspring. Why this is so will have to be the subject of more study.

What can we do to boost our spiritual security and nurture our instinctual selves? Besides relying on traditional methods, such as a certain faith or religious practice, I recommend a therapeutic touch in the form of simple back rubs from your spouse or even massage by a Registered Massage Therapist. At least during those moments, we can free our minds of stressful thoughts and let our physical selves benefit from the healing energy of another's hands. Meditation, feared by some as too off-beat, is really just a simple kind of self-hypnosis which can open mental pathways to increased serenity. Countless infertile persons have endorsed these techniques, along with exercise to reduce that frazzled and out-of-control feeling. We will cover these strategies, and others, in a section on stress.

Our Thoughts and Feelings...

Our Thoughts and Feelings...

DO MEN REACT TO INFERTILITY DIFFERENTLY FROM WOMEN?

The Male Perspective.

Do men experience infertility the same way women do? Couples are frequently confused about the difference between the woman and the man in coping with fertility impairment. Keep in mind that both genders are deeply affected by reproductive loss, however, men are usually not as expressive about the loss. We know that men, even in our modern era, are socialized to be stoic, not to cry. Even if the husband has a sperm imperfection, he may feel the typical shock, anger, denial, etc., but rarely does he show his emotions to the same extent the wife does.

In the couples' groups I have led, the women commonly carry the emotional intensity in the beginning sessions. Regardless of which person in the couple has the infertility diagnosis, the husband usually feels it is his task to be optimistic in spite of his wife's pessimism. "He is the rational, the logical one, I'm the emotional one," say many infertile wives. As time goes by and the husbands realize and accept the extent of their own grief, they are able to express their feelings more readily. The remarkable effect of the men accepting one another's grief is tremendous reinforcement for their showing honest feelings. By the final group meeting, the men at times, disclose their grief more than the women.

Mike

A couple in their mid-thirties, Annie and Mike, joined a newly formed support group. Their diagnosis was unexplained infertility. Annie had to "talk Mike into coming to the group" the first time. He couldn't see what they were going to gain by talking to other people who were as miserable as he and Annie were. Mike was quiet during the first session. Gradually he spoke more often. By the fourth meeting he came without his wife. "She had to work but I didn't want to miss this." In fact, Mike was always the first person to arrive, usually 5 minutes early, to make sure the group had enough chairs. Often he started the discussion and offered support to the other members.

A few years later, with two children in tow, he told me how much he learned from the group especially regarding expressing his feelings, the ones he thought were too negative to admit. He said the ability to talk to the men in the group about personal things enabled him to express himself better to men and women in his everyday life.

Mike's story is a typical example of how men hold back when it comes to painful feelings from infertility. Partly accounting for their seeming distance is the social myth that men don't whine and whimper. Secondly, the primary role of males, even today, is that of provider – man must have his work, while the primary role of the female, still, is motherhood. When we are role conscious, we feel, as women, we have missed the boat or our boat is sinking fast, whereas the male still has his work. In addition, as many women attest, we as women, feel the menstrual cramps signaling another "failure", feel the mood swings from Pergonal and live minute by minute those days before a pregnancy test.

Husbands are by nature somewhat removed from the immediate intensity of the treatment ordeals, but when we really listen to them they tell us how painful the experience is for them, as well. They too have dreams of their almost children, they mourn the miscarriage and remember the anniversaries. Most of all, they loathe the agony that they see their wives endure month after month. More often than not, they feel responsible, even if they have no actual impairment.

The male partner's reply to his mate's grief is often the "fix it" response in which he will try to make the pain go away for the woman by giving her solutions that work for him, i.e., distraction, logic and problem-solving. Women, of course, have cognitive resources to think rationally but something comes between logic and inner feelings so that the logic doesn't stick. I picture a slab of concrete that truncates a woman's logic from adequately influencing her feelings. Most men I know can be hurt by an interpersonal episode, but say to themselves "I can't expect everyone to like my idea" or "It didn't work this time, let's take a break and think of a new option." In general, women can think and say those exact words, but our feelings of grief, sometimes failure, remain undaunted.

Like women, men vary in the degree of their desire for a child, from "It's okay if we don't have children, my wife and I will have a happy life together regardless," to "If we don't have children, life will lose its meaning for me," but I rarely see this latter reaction. In short, the male perspective is as varied as the female perspective, though often not seen as quite so determined because of differences in role perception. In addition, men have been taught to behave in certain ways and are not sidetracked by maternal drive.

An exception to the cavalier male attitude toward infertility, however, exists in the men who know they are sterile. Not surprisingly, this diagnosis is much harder to accept. I find that these men carry intense emotions and sorrow for longer periods of time. They may be haunted by a defective self-concept. They may perceive they are not equal to other men and sometimes these feelings make marital relationships problematic. Naturally if and when they want to please their wives with biological children they must agree to sperm donor insemination which carries another whole set of complex issues. The secret of *azospermia* usually becomes a terrible burden that the husband feels he must bear, to save himself and his children from being stigmatized. Wives, however, are usually quite comfortable with the donor sperm option, except in a minority of cases in which the wife voices that she feels as though she has had an affair with another man. This infidelity notion, however, abates as the wife becomes more comfortable with the idea of the donor gamete and begins to bond with her concept of the developing embryo.

Although secrecy about donor sperm has been the norm throughout the history of insemination, there is now a trend toward registration of sperm donors, especially in Europe where men volunteer to be identified in case the recipient family needs more information on the child's genetic background. Openness where donor eggs are concerned is controversial, but egg donor recipients are much more willing to disclose this information to their children. These topics will be addressed in a planned sequel to this book.

As mentioned earlier, one of the most effective ways for men to deal with infertility or sterility is to discuss their feelings in the safety of a support group. Several men I have counseled have shown interest in a men's support group, especially concerning the use of donor sperm, but we have a difficult time getting enough men to commit to group meetings. The factors mentioned before, such as role constraints about expressing feelings and needing to appear in control and rational, may come into play. In my experience, support groups can be equally effective whether they are composed of all women, all men or a mixture of both, even when some individuals join without their spouses. The following section describes in detail the magic of support groups.

SHOULD WE JOIN A SUPPORT GROUP?

Sharing with others brings affirmation.

I heartily recommend a support group for many reasons: information sharing, problem-solving, camaraderie, but most of all because when someone else says out loud the very thing you have been struggling with – what better self-affirmation? "I couldn't have said it better myself!" becomes a common and comforting thought. Support groups for infertility patients while undergoing medical treatment are offered free of charge at some Fertility Centers. Our local RESOLVE chapters sponsor time limited support groups led by professionals at reduced cost. If you and others you know about would like to start your own support group, you may follow these guidelines:

1. When you've procured a commitment of 8-10 people, decide on a convenient time and place on the same day every week.

2. Decide with the members how many weeks you would like the group to meet.

3. At the first meeting, discuss the confidentiality of information divulged in the group. Ask everyone to promise to attend every meeting except for dire emergencies, otherwise the group's cohesion will be reduced. Decide what the group wants to do if one or more of the members gets pregnant while the group is meeting. Discuss what everyone thinks about members meeting socially after the group sessions are over.

4. For your first topic of discussion, ask members to tell their infertility story. In this way, people will get to know each other in a less threatening way.

5. Allow and accept all feelings. Try to understand, offer support, not judgment.

6. The group will generate its own topics and set its own pace. There is no right way to do it.

I hope you'll give a group a chance. Here is an article, written by Linda Cagnetti, which appeared in a RESOLVE newsletter. It gives you a participant's perspective.

A Gift To Myself

When I signed up to attend a RESOLVE support group, I had no idea what to expect. I hoped I'd find some kind of help in dealing with the emotional side of my infertility. I could find little written on the topic; I couldn't talk with close friends about it because they didn't understand; and I didn't know anyone else with an infertility problem well enough to disclose my increasing distress and frustration.

My infertility was affecting the quality of my life and undermining my emotional well being. I was ashamed of some of my feelings. Confused by them. Did anyone else in the world share them, I wondered? The whole world seemed pregnant. I was jealous of others' children. I was angry when my friends announced pregnancies and agonized that I was letting my husband down. I hated people who tiptoed around the topic. I began avoiding christenings, and baby showers became agony. I quit making life plans, rationalizing I could do nothing until "This" was resolved. I put on an optimistic front, but most of the time I was sad, and often close to despair.

If nothing else, I reasoned, I'd go to the group meeting, listen, and find out how abnormal and irrational I was compared with others. And maybe, I reasoned, I could learn how others cope with their childlessness and go on with their lives.

Along with six other women, whom I'd never met, I committed an hour and a half of my time, one night a week for eight weeks, and $64 to pay professional group leaders (a counselor and a psychiatric nurse, both of whom had infertility problems and worked professionally with others who did). One of the group members invited us to meet in her home.

At first, the meetings were a bit awkward. Other members, I discovered, had no idea what to expect either. But the leaders informally and expertly got us started. The only requirements were regular attendance and strict adherence to starting and finishing times. No one was forced to talk. The leaders suggested a dozen or so topics, but we chose them, usually based on what had happened to one of us during the week.

It seemed, almost by fate, that the eight of us represented every problem of infertility. We had women who'd never been pregnant, those who'd suffered miscarriages, those who'd adopted children or had adoptions fall through, and secondary infertility. Plus we were all at different stages in dealing with our problem.

Slowly, each week, like peeling layers from an onion, we learned to trust each other, to open up, to reveal our stories and our frustrations. We began to bond, cemented by our common plight.

*We talked about everything related to our infertility –
our sexuality, family attitudes, motivations for children,
breast-feeding, and doctors. We sometimes laughed at the
absurdity of what we were going through – early morning
treks with specimens, and our life-long companion, the
basal thermometer.*

*We talked about what hurts and what helps. We talked
about miscarriages and fears of adoption and eternal
hope.*

*For the first time, some of us identified our feelings –
anger, lethargy, grief – and our particular vulnerabilities.
Here, once a week, we had a safe place to express our
repressed feelings, in a supportive, empathic and non-
judgmental forum. Here we could be totally honest. The
group allowed us to vent our feelings, sometimes helping
to dissipate the intensity of them. The group gave us
unspoken permission to grieve and to lament our losses.*

*We found ourselves "trying on" each other's coping
methods. By listening and talking, we discovered other
prisms through which to interpret what was happening
to us.*

*We found no magic solutions or resolutions. But we
found relief from our emotional isolation. We found we
had something to give to each other – comfort and*

encouragement—the kind no one else could provide for us.

We spent the first sessions exploring feelings and attitudes. Then some of us started searching for ways to accept this block in our life dreams and go around it. We began exploring, with each other's way to restore emotional equilibrium and perspective to our daily lives. Each group member seemed to grow or change ever so slightly, in a different way. For some, it was the simple matter of acknowledging and feeling okay about their anger and vowing to avoid baby showers without guilt. For others, it was a decision to pursue adoption.

We witnessed and celebrated the slightest progress with pride, and love. Soon, we were lingering over our iced tea long after the leaders had gone and the meeting was formally over. We found more and more to talk about. And our bond continued to grow. When the eight weeks were over, we planned another meeting, and then another. We were reluctant to let go of our new friendships.

We continue to reach out to each other, and inquire of each other's ups and downs. We telephone and sometimes we visit.

Did the group experience rid us of our "old friend infertility" or our sadness? No. It'll always be a part of us, we suspect. Nothing will fill the void. But we now know how to comfort ourselves a bit, where to turn when we lose our equilibrium again, and again.

For me, the support group was one of the best presents I ever gave to myself. A priceless gift for which I'll be eternally grateful.

For more information on support groups call my office at 513-721-1500 or RESOLVE, Inc. at 617-623-0744. Or write to RESOLVE Inc., 1310 Broadway, Somerville, MA., 02144.

Our Thoughts and Feelings...

Our Thoughts and Feelings...

WHAT ABOUT SECONDARY INFERTILITY?

Resolving guilt about wanting more children.

Kristin

Kristin came to my office for the fourth time in two months. With tears in her eyes she said, "I can't accept this! My pregnancy test was negative again. Why could I get pregnant and deliver a beautiful son five years ago and since then be unable to bear children? The doctors say my eggs are fine, Charles has great sperm. Our son, Nicholas, is so disappointed, he wanted a little brother or sister so badly. What do I tell him?"

Kristin is a talented writer and extremely compassionate woman and I've seen what a wonderful mother she is to Nick. But now she was overwrought with grief, guilt and anger. "I wish I could explain what this feels like, what's scary is this hurts almost as much as it did before Nick, but without him I would be almost suicidal."

Some of you, like Kristin, have one child who is living or perhaps has died and want to have another. The secondarily infertile have a particular dilemma. Can the primary infertile understand and accept the secondary infertile's position? Not really. Can the fertile person empathize? Again, not exactly. Unfortunately, there are not many forums for this group of people from which to gain support, so this population suffers in a unique way.

Even though we have one child, for whom we are extremely grateful, we often yearn to give our child a brother or sister. We feel guilty depriving our child of siblings, resulting in the revisitation of our old friends, *hopelessness* and *helplessness*. Kristin, still crying, voices, "I'm so ashamed in front of these couples who have no children that I want a second child, but I need a support group, too. Fertile people tell me I should stop at one since I had so much trouble getting him. Infertile people can't listen at all, they tell me they would be completely happy with just one healthy child."

Grieving Children

Your child, if you have told him or her or even if you haven't, will grieve in his or her own way whenever you suffer a loss. Encourage your child to express his or her feelings, ask you questions and most importantly play with you. Your child's play shows, in a predominant way, what is on his or her mind and in his or her heart. Little girls will need a family of dolls, little boys may prefer action figures. Assure your child that he or she is not to blame for mommy's sadness or the loss of the baby or failed pregnancy test. If your child regresses, shows behavior more befitting of a child much younger, tell him or her you understand and not to worry. We all regress when we are grieving. The behaviors will stop when we feel better.

Five year old Maddie is a case in point. When her first sibling was born dead, she expressed her grief by forgetting how to use the bathroom, drawing with markers on her abdomen, asking her mother if everyone in the family was going to die.

Spend extra time holding and hugging your child. Let him talk about how much he wanted a brother. Tell him you appreciate his honesty and understanding. He won't comprehend the meaning of death until he reaches the age of reason (about 12 years old) but he'll still have plenty of questions and fears about it. He may want to depict his feelings in drawings. If appropriate, tell his teachers and other critical people in his life that he is going through stress. He won't want to leave your side.

There is support out there for those of you who want more children. In local RESOLVE chapters, many members and organizers are in your predicament. In fact, the founder of the Greater Cincinnati RESOLVE chapter, as well as her successor, each had one biological child and tried for years to have others. They put a terrific amount of energy into building the chapter, recruiting other infertile persons who volunteered to support others, all the while coping  with the frustration of secondary infertility. Many editions of RESOLVE newsletters are devoted to couples with secondary infertility. We may surmise that having the first child gave these women the impetus and hope to form a larger group of people who needed information and support. The most promising pathway through the grief of secondary infertility is fellowship with people in the same circumstances. This can most easily be accomplished through networking with the coordinators of your local RESOLVE, Inc.

HOW WOULD WE KNOW IF WE NEED PROFESSIONAL COUNSELING?

The crisis of infertility can overwhelm us.

My belief is that any interaction with an empathic person can help us grow, most of us can thrive on the understanding and acceptance of a spouse, family member, or friend. Sometimes, however, the crisis of infertility can overwhelm even the "strongest", well-supported person, and no shame should be associated with seeking professional assistance.

If you, or a person you love, shows signs of serious depression such as insomnia, abnormal weight loss, extreme anxiety, inability to function at work or at home, use of alcohol or drugs to ease the emotional pain, or any talk of suicide, a professional counselor should be sought. You are entitled to interview the mental health professional, regardless of the discipline, to determine how much the individual understands about the biomedical and psychosocial facets of infertility and whether he or she has had experience working with infertile persons who are in your phase of the treatment or resolution. Take a grief partner with you to help you ask the right questions. Tell the therapist what you want from the therapy. Negotiate the fee before or during the first session. If you are not satisfied with the professional's approach, you can find someone who has the qualifications and approach you need. You may also want to contact your physician, your clergy or other helpful persons you trust. Again, use the resources of RESOLVE, Inc. to find established professionals.

Our Thoughts and Feelings...

ALTERNATIVES OFFER RESOLUTION

Can We Expedite the Process? How Do We Assess Our Progress Toward Resolution?

Sometimes infertile persons ask this question soon after I meet them, others wait until they are in a crisis state. The answer is that you cannot force yourself to think about the next step until you are ready to think about it. Readiness is a critical ingredient of change. Emotional, social and psychological factors in each of us determine our readiness to accept a new idea.

To use adoption as an example, countless numbers of infertile patients have felt insulted if their doctors suggest they apply for adoption. Tom and Faye, trying to conceive for six years, perceived the doctor's comment as "giving up" on them. They call her "heartless" to mention the solution that most of their friends and family have already promoted – the solution that makes them feel sick inside.

Most of us, as you well know, grow up believing we

will have biological progeny. We are truly shocked to think that we won't have these children. Virtually nobody wakes up in the morning and thinks, "I don't want my genetic kids, I want to adopt a child." The idea of adopting comes easily to only a select few. The rest of us must grapple with the concept, grieve, examine our motives and so on. All of this takes time, maybe years. Faye and Tom are not ready to consider adoption at the particular stage they are in. Their feelings are neither right nor wrong, they simply are.

Nobody has to tell an infertile couple to think about adoption. They already know about adoption and will ask more about the process when they are ready. It's only human to fear the unknown. When we are still in a state of fear about adoption, A.R.T., (Assisted Reproductive Technologies), donor gametes and child-free choices, we cannot accept these alternatives.

The point is, you will know when you are ready to discuss these options. After meeting with hundreds of infertile clients, I've learned that every new step a couple takes in infertility treatment takes a specific amount of time for assimilation; the time is governed by the feelings, the grief, of the people involved. As with grief, we can't rush the process of decision making about reproduction.

ASSESS WHERE YOU ARE IN YOUR PROGRESS TOWARD RESOLUTION.

A. HAVE WE CONSIDERED ALL OF THE TREAT-MENT ALTERNATIVES THAT WOULD HELP US HAVE A GENETIC CHILD?

_____Yes   _____No

1. How far are we willing to go?

_____

_____

_____

_____

_____

2. Are there technologies we won't accept?

_____

_____

_____

_____

_____

3. How will we allow ourselves to stop treatment keeping in mind our emotional equilibrium and physical stamina.

_____

_____

_____

_____

_____

B. WOULD WE CONSIDER DONOR GAMETES?

1. Are we thinking about using a donor egg so that the wife will be the biologic mother but have no genetic link?

_____Yes   _____No

_____

_____

2. Are we considering donor sperm?

_____Yes   _____No

_____

_____

3. Are we considering both donor egg and donor sperm?

_____Yes   _____No

_____

_____

In some cases, fertility centers allow an in vitro fertilization patient to donate some of her eggs to a woman whose eggs are impaired and needs donor eggs. In this way both women pay a significantly lower fee for their respective treatments.

C. WILL WE CONSIDER ADOPTING A CHILD?
There are myriad ways of adopting babies and older children in the nineties.

_____

_____

_____

_____

_____

D. WOULD WE EMBRACE A CHILD-FREE
LIFESTYLE?

Keep in mind that couples I've known who
are child-free are not childless. More often,
the partners are surrounded by children of
friends and family, and take a great deal of
initiative in children's lives. You may want to
read **Sweet Grapes** by Carter and Carter
who chose this option and describe the pros
and cons.

_____

_____

_____

_____

_____

E. SHALL WE PURSUE SURROGATE PARENTING?

_____Yes   _____No

_____

_____

F. WHAT ARE SOME PRACTICAL CONSTRAINTS?

1. What is the most we can spend on these
pursuits?

_____

_____

_____

_____

_____

2. Do we have a time frame that will help us
   keep control over these years of our lives?

_____

_____

_____

_____

_____

G. CAN WE SET A REGULAR TIME, SAY 30
   MINUTES ONCE A WEEK ON SUNDAY
   EVENING, TO REVIEW OUR OPTIONS?

            _____Yes   _____No

   If "no" when can we discuss?_____

_____

_____

After pondering these questions, you and your spouse
will want to examine what effect your choice will have on
your lives at present and at various points in the future.

While you may be anxious to read more about these
alternatives, it is important that we discuss the unique
stresses felt by those with impaired fertility. You will learn
to deal with the increased emotional strains and stress
responses, then you can make clear decisions on how to
proceed. Let's examine this issue next.

**PEAKS OF INTENSE STRESS
VALLEYS OF DISCOVERY**

WHY IS BEING INFERTILE SO STRESSFUL?

Celeste's Story.

Yesterday I returned a call to a woman in crisis. Celeste is a professor of genetics in a local university. Literally screaming with anger, she said, "Why can't I do this simple thing that any female starting  at eleven years old can do? My colleagues say they just look at their boyfriends and get pregnant! I'm so sick of this! I don't deserve this; I've never done anything to deserve this. Why is this happening to me?" Celeste had just been told that her twentieth pregnancy test was negative. "For five years that damn test has been negative, so why does the news knock me down every time? When am I going to feel better?"

Celeste went on to say that she felt as though she were a failure, she had failed her husband, her parents, herself. She once thought of herself as serene, even tempered, now she said she flew off the handle at the slightest provocation. "I'm not sure who I am anymore!"

Celeste's story is all too common in the women I see who feel they have failed to provide for their families and themselves the most fundamental of all human experiences, giving birth and parenting the cherished child of their dreams. In her voice, I could hear self-blame, guilt, feelings of inadequacy, shame, despair and, of course, anger. These unwanted feelings, naturally, generate tremendous stress. Celeste is in a state of acute grief which, as you know, affects her mind, body and spirit. The impact of these repeated losses tend to accumulate so that her self-concept is distorted and diminished. The strong and competent academician she formerly perceived herself to be is a perception no longer available to her, at least not now.

With time, the shock and anger associated with those words, *the test was negative*, will dissipate as hope for another chance, another cycle, another baby will emerge. The chronic grief, however, will most likely remain and plateau until a baby is born or another loss is sustained. I believe that women and men, like you, who suffer impairments in fertility carry additional levels of stress. It, as they say, goes with the territory. Grief is stressful. It's as simple and as complicated as that. If we were to draw a time line of hypothetical average stress on people in their reproductive years, then a line depicting all the stress on a so-called average infertile person in treatment, I would see it as follows:

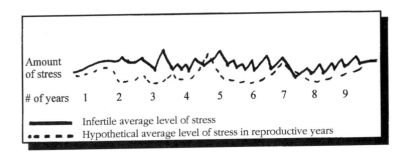

Amount
of stress

# of years   1   2   3   4   5   6   7   8   9

━━━━━━ Infertile average level of stress
■ ■ ■ ■ Hypothetical average level of stress in reproductive years

The peaks of intense stress are higher, the recovery periods never reaching the peace of mind that we need in order to function optimally in our everyday worlds.

With Celeste's story in mind, let us examine in this chapter the factors in infertility which may increase the stress response. Secondly, we will see how understanding basic stress management strategies related to infertility can decrease the effect of stress on all facets of our lives.

Our Thoughts and Feelings...

THE UNIQUE STRESSORS OF FERTILITY IMPAIRMENTS

Voicing our feelings.

It hurts all the time, no matter where we are.

The chronic pain, the grief of infertility is always with you. The media bombards you with images of precious children, sometimes in splendid circumstances, but other times abused or even murdered. It all hurts. It pains us when we visit the fertility doctor and twenty pregnant ladies, some with small children, are discussing their weight or how much fun it is to feel their babies kick. It hurts at work where everyone else is either pregnant or has three kids at home. It hurts at parties where circles of people discuss their children's schools. The sense of being unequal, left out, pervades our consciousness in religious services, outdoor activities, restaurants, etc. For many women, just going out of their homes is an act of bravery, for they are sure to be faced with more grief, more stress.

Infertility is such a great emotional stress that a group

of patients surveyed by a fertility program reported that stress was the number one reason for leaving infertility treatment.

Incidentally, some research shows a trend that women who have documented organic impairments such as blocked tubes, misshapen uterus, and other problems seen on x-ray or during laparoscopy, feel relatively less stress than women who have unexplained infertility. The rationale is that if there is no explanation, that woman is more apt to blame herself and thus put more pressure on herself to be perfect. The unexplained diagnosis may carry more angst.

My stress is insidious! It seems to have gotten control of me.
Often we don't realize we're under that much stress. We tell ourselves that our predicament is not a life-and-death matter. Our friends and family tell us not to take our problems so seriously. Our family doctors tell us to relax and it will happen. I remember, after three years of trying to conceive, I sought the advice of a noted endocrinologist at a large university. He told me I was wasting my time, that infertility was not a medical problem and maybe I should consider myself lucky that I have only <u>that</u> problem. I was dismayed, my worries had been discounted and I felt I was doing something wrong by caring about my reproductive losses.

Sometimes, we don't accept the extent of our stress until we behave more or less outrageously, as in the case of Celeste, who bellowed her feelings over the phone the day she felt she went "over the edge." Suffice it to say, the stress was real. Reproductive loss can be devastating and the deaths of babies are tragic. You are decidedly under great stress, your reaction is probably normal, and you deserve understanding. You are likely experiencing decreased self-esteem, impaired body image, and sexuality upheavals.

Infertility has bashed my self-esteem. It has me questioning my worth.

"If I can't make babies, what good am I?" Incomprehensibly, these remarks are made by obviously outstanding women, even today. "What will I do if I can't be a mother?" said Celeste, whose research in genetics was known nationally. Few other handicaps as rampant as this one result in a woman feeling totally useless. Of course, this destructive self-talk isn't logical, we know that, but the feelings remain.

Infertility has made me a damaged person. I really don't like myself.

"I feel like a broken toy, my husband got a dud, he should divorce me" was the persistent belief of a home-maker in a women's support group I led twelve years ago. You would, or maybe wouldn't, be surprised at how many wonderful women today echo those self-deprecating comments to me or to their husbands. "My body has betrayed me, I hate it, I'm ugly."

The enormous pressure these bereaved women put on themselves to be perfect, to somehow compensate on the outside for the ugliness they see inside, is just one more stressor.

Can it be only a coincidence that most infertile women are meticulously groomed, exceedingly well dressed, eat and exercise properly, present them-selves in an affable manner? Sometimes the expectations we hold for ourselves far exceed what fertile women hold, or almost anyone around us, for that matter. Our houses must look well-kept, our gardens well maintained, we even try to keep our dogs looking good. These are all attempts, I believe, to help us feel better about ourselves and our lives in the absence of children. At least we can do these things right. In spite of our efforts, the search for perfection never really works, we always feel less than adequate. That kind of stress, too, is always there.

There is stress piled upon stress. It is overwhelming.

Like any other invisible handicap or chronic illness, the infertile person's chronic stress persists in the face of the regular and extraordinary stressors we all experience. As if day-to-day stress weren't enough, we are faced with the additional unexpected stress events in our lives such as deaths of parents, failed careers, or even dealing with issues such as alcoholism or surviving sexual abuse. So what happens to the stress levels? Of course they accumulate and seem to take on gargantuan proportions.

Pressure mounts for us to make a decision about the way we will handle our infertility. Each of the choices has its own stress and, in turn, its own questions. *How will we handle the thought of a donor egg or sperm? How do I feel about frozen embryos? What do we tell the children?* For example, for those of us who move on to in vitro fertilization or even third party reproduction, while our options for having children increase, the stress seems to grow more complicated, also. It is imperative that we find ways to handle the stress of infertility.

Our Thoughts and Feelings...

HANDLING THE STRESSORS OF FERTILITY IMPAIRMENT

With stress reduction techniques we can handle it.

Stress reduction is the topic most often requested by groups of infertile people, from my experience. Now that we have reviewed the reasons that we are under a great deal of stress, let's find the most effective stress reducing strategies for each of us. My recommendation is regular, individual de-stressing activities within a framework of a highly developed social support network.

Basic Mind-Body Techniques

The individual de-stressing activities for women and men include simple meditation, yoga or breathing exercises, progressive muscle relaxation, imaging, and so forth.

A different but also effective method for finding inner peace is releasing energy in the form of aerobics, competitive sports, jogging, dancing. These conditioning activities, though, must be curtailed for women during certain infertility treatments, so swimming or upper body weight resistance might provide some benefit.

Mind-body techniques include activities which specifically express certain feelings such as dancing, singing, using artistic talent by drawing or painting. Any self-expressive activity can reduce stress to some degree. Let's not forget outdoor activities, like fishing or hiking, to promote serenity.

Finding Supportive People

For fear of sounding like a broken record, I'll refer you back to section one where I emphasize the critical need for empathic listeners. If accepting and non-judgmental people are hard to find in your families and community of friends, and you've tried to teach them how to listen without giving advice, consider joining a support group or starting one yourself.

Journaling

As I've mentioned before, another effective strategy is journaling, a popular term for keeping an old-fashioned diary. Taking the time to document our thoughts, feelings, and activities helps us gain perspective. Taking time for ourselves, attending to our wishes and fears, increases a sense of self-caring which is deficient in some of us. I recently read about a study showing that journaling bolsters the immune system. Since we know that stress will depress the immune system, we can presume that controlling stress would improve the success of our cells to ward off illnesses.

Managing Time

Managing time is always a challenge in our hectic lives which often feel overwhelming. Covey's paradigm from **Seven Habits of Highly Effective People** is useful in setting priorities and implementing plans. It looks something like this...

1	Urgent and Important	3	Important Not Urgent
2	Urgent and Unimportant	4	Not Urgent or Important

Can you see in which quadrant you spend most of your time? Many of us spend too much time in quadrant 4, mainly because we can't say *no* to the little distractions of our surroundings. An example of quadrant 2 would be the phone ringing. An instance of *Important Not Urgent* would be taking the car in for an oil change. The trouble is, we may treat everything we do as urgent and important, which surely increases our overall stress levels.

Another graphic way of looking at our lives to gain perspective is the life grid, described by Jeffers in **Feel the Fear and Do It Anyway**. Picture a simple grid consisting of 9-12 spaces. In each space write a facet of your life, or a goal for that matter. These may be marriage, career, caretaking of parents, religious activities, developing musical talent, homemaking, leisure activities, maintenance of friendships, exercise and nutrition program, and of course, desire for children and infertility treatment. The author's point is that when you see one grid which is shaky, you must put it in perspective as only a part of the whole. You may be saying to yourself, "It sounds good on paper, but..." and I agree. The grief and stress of infertility permeates all aspects of our lives, but if we can try to keep ideas such as this one in our minds, we may find some reassurance in them.

Irrational Beliefs

We unwittingly create stress for ourselves by employing irrational beliefs. A salient example that comes to mind is the all too common belief that <u>we cause our infertility</u>, either by thought or deed.

Sondra

Sondra believes her unexplained infertility was a punishment by God because she had an abortion at age 17. Her parents coerced her into the decision, but she knows she could not have handled a baby at that stage of her life.

Still, she regards her inner self as unworthy and at times, dirty.

Jennifer

A particularly poignant story was that of Jennifer, who at 19 was raped and beaten at knife point. Although rationally she can't imagine how anything she did invited the rapist to attack her, she nevertheless had a haunting suspicion that she caused the rape and the rapist scarred her reproductive organs.

Irrational thoughts which raise our stress arise when we hear those flip remarks that the armchair psychologists are happy to offer. *Well, some people weren't cut out to be parents... you just have to accept not having children.* Not only are these remarks insensitive and discounting, their poison sometimes sinks into our subconscious mind and we begin to believe them. Other irrational thoughts, not necessarily related to infertility, but applicable nonetheless, are notions such as *Everyone I meet must like me. I will put in 100% effort in everything I do. I should help everyone who asks me.* You see, I am sure, how these beliefs are not only unrealistic, but also create horrific exhaustion. Often, fertile people do, however, strive to be perfect in hopes that their reward will be a healthy baby. Isn't it a vicious cycle? We are so hard on ourselves.

You and your spouse will think of many other irrational beliefs that you hold in common. The best way to rid your mind of them is to talk to people who care, tell them and yourself your illogical thoughts, write them in your journal, then replace those thoughts with constructive ones. *I did not cause my infertility, we just don't know right now why I can't carry a baby. There is no shame in being infertile. Murderers are able to have children, so if God was going to punish me, why wouldn't He punish them and make them infertile? Nobody can be liked by everyone* and, of course, *Nobody's perfect.*

Positive Affirmations

These positive self statements may seem a bit corny to you, but you may feel better if you tell yourself, out loud, "I am a worthy person.... I don't have to be perfect. I am loved and loveable." Similarly, "I was meant to be a parent. I love children and I will make a wonderful parent." Doesn't it make sense that we need to reinforce these positive messages to counteract the sarcastic and ignorant remarks some people make to us? Some people put self-affirming notes around the house and office to remind themselves of their worth. Self-affirmations are particularly effective if we can say them in a calm, even meditative state of mind, if we can image ourselves as loving and lovable people.

Meditation and Imaging

Even if you don't like the idea of meditating, I want to

ask you to try a simple exercise for ten minutes each morning and evening. The book **Relaxation Response** describes a technique which a Harvard psychiatrist, in 1975, studied and found to be more efficient in lowering vital signs and producing a calm feeling than any other meditative technique at that time. I've been suggesting this method to my clients for over 15 years with successful outcomes.

The technique is quite simple. You sit comfortably, close your eyes, and each time you exhale you say in your mind, "One." After you try this a few times you'll find it relatively easy to complete. While you are relaxing, you could imagine yourself in a lovely spot, or see yourself using positive affirmations. There is nothing mystical about this strategy, it happens on a physiological plane which naturally brings a degree of peace of mind. Of course, meditation does not cause conception or successful implantation to occur. The purpose of these tools is for us to reach an optimum level of physiological and psychological health. These measures, along with the usual guidelines of good nutrition, adequate rest, and exercise, will help us cope with this roller coaster with which we're so familiar. In a recent workshop on *Managing Stress With Infertility*, we asked instructors of Chinese Internal Arts to present demonstrations of T'ai Chi Ch'uan, meant to induce a relaxation response, enhance deep-level brain wave activity and improve overall health. I suspect some of these ancient practices will become even more acceptable in our modern, high stress era.

Primitive Notions

Do you recall when *Worry Dolls*, the tiny cloth and string figures sewn together, were popular? You might still see them in shops which feature ethnic knickknacks. They purportedly mollified worries when you told the dolls your troubles. The worry jar and the worry chair allegedly accomplish the same job, that is, we set aside a place to contain our troubles. In the worry jar, we place small pieces of paper on which we have written our most troublesome and private fears. We may occasionally take the slips of paper out and read them to find that some of them are no longer relevant or some we aren't worried about any more.

Since you know you may worry every day about infertility, you can put boundaries on the time you spend worrying, which can decrease your stress. That is to say, for example, you do your worrying for the day, all at once, for ten minutes in your worry chair at 6:00 p.m. Then you can relegate new worries to the next night instead of tolerating them throughout your day. The effect of this tactic is that we have a bit more control over our problems, and we can encapsulate the concerns by limiting our attention to them. Though quick and easy, these practices have one important concept in common, that is they allow us time to attend to our inner selves which, once again, promotes de-stressing.

Last but not least, I'll mention, once again, the value (for some of us) of a pet. You've probably seen reports of men and women who acquire animals in an attempt to lower their blood pressures. Of course, only you would know if stroking a pet's fur can bring you a sense of calm, but frequently, people I have counseled found that loving a pet increased their overall sense of well being.

In conclusion, we have no doubt, in most circumstances, that our stressors as a result of infertility are tremendous, insidious, and diminish our self-image, our sexuality, and our coping power as we meet further complexities in more refined technologies of reproduction. We can handle the stress using basic de-stressing techniques, finding supportive people, confronting our irrational beliefs, and increasing control and balance in our lives by following simple worry-busting strategies outlined in this chapter. I welcome feedback on these practices and hope they work well for you.

Our Thoughts and Feelings...

FOR BETTER <u>AND</u> FOR WORSE

CAN THIS MARRIAGE THRIVE DESPITE INFERTILITY?

Sharing the worst of times bonds couples closer.

When we make our vows, we never anticipate that the *worst of times* are ever going to be as traumatic as those we experience as an infertile couple. Nevertheless, the testimony of most infertile couples I see is that, if you put your heartache together with your spouse's, the relationship doesn't suffer, the reciprocal empathy brings the couple closer. If your union can survive the death of children, it can survive anything.

The unexpected twists and turns of infertility present *fertile* ground, however, for exploring how well you can argue and make up. Experts on relationships contend that verbal fighting in marriages is not only normal, it's healthy. If two people have no disagreements, they are not being honest with one another. The way we really get to know our spouse is to work out our differences with him or her. It is important to know the "ground rules" though, in order to have healthy arguments.

1. Understand that there are rocky roads ahead.

In the arena of infertility, new choices must be dealt with constantly. Shall we pursue this treatment, that medication? The premise that opposites attract is generally true in relationships. The couple boasts in the courtship phase how similar they are; in fact, they believe they share most ideas and things in common. Later they recognize their differing stance on many issues. The differences are, indeed, healthy. *Individuation* in the relationship has occurred. The spouses complement each other. Once the differences are recognized, accepted, and honored, the marriage becomes even more solid. There is room to grow. The spouses begin to process each challenge in their unique way. Maybe she voices her preference first, then he may agree or think of a different approach. Each change in treatment takes a certain amount of time to digest and in the healthy relationship, the one who comes to a quick judgment waits for the more ponderous partner.

2. There <u>are</u> basic gender differences.

In most infertile couples I've known, the desire for children is not exactly equal, usually the wife is more tenacious in her wish for offspring. She usually says she has to have children or she'll never be satisfied; the husband often says he'd be okay spending the rest of his life with her, although children would be icing on the cake. In this brief synopsis of stated differences, we shall uncover a cornucopia of unstated feelings.

As I've written again and again, there is no discounting the magnitude of the maternal drive, which, I believe, explains most of the woman's intense desire for children. The husband, however, usually feels hurt that she cannot feel the same as he, that is, satisfied with only him. The wife, too, is unhappy that her husband cannot be as intense about having children as she. Fortunately, this tension between them is abated when I reassure them that they are experiencing the same feelings that most couples have. Since many people do not have the opportunity to attend a support group, I believe they are helped by hearing about the experience of others and thus feeling their problems are universal, i.e., they are not a "crazy" couple.

The goal is for both to perceive the other's position. He is encouraged to fully express to her the sadness he feels of not being able to be a daddy when he wanted to and his fear of maybe never being able to have a biological child. She, too, can empathize with how he must feel when she pushes for a baby and seems to discount him. Both need to practice understanding and honoring the other's feelings.

3. Fighting is <u>only</u> healthy when you fight fair.
Communicating honestly and debating in good faith leads to positive resolutions. Fighting fair means listening more than talking, taking time to understand the other's

positions before stating your own, discussing only the feelings and issues at hand, not dredging up grudges from the past. Trying to forgive is essential. "I forgive you" is one of the most freeing phrases in our language, yet it's so hard to say. Likewise, frequently saying "Thank you" to our spouse does not come as easily to some of us as it does to others.

4. It is important to express the "I" position.

A simple but effective way of expressing our desires or hurts is beginning your conversation with I. For example, "I want you to sit down and talk with me." Or, "I feel discouraged when you look at your book while I'm talking with you."

By opening conversations with the "I" statement, you take responsibility for your feelings without blaming the other. You don't put your spouse on the defensive by saying something like, "There you go again, reading a book while I'm talking to you. You are so rude."

Also important in this practice is giving your feedback with positive requests for specific behavior, such as, "You know, I feel so valued when you put down the newspaper and look straight into my eyes," or "I feel appreciated when you ask me if I want my neck rubbed. Thank you."

When approaching your mate with a sensitive topic,

take care to respect his or her circumstances at a given time. If she is typically very tired after nine o'clock at night, your request for a behavior change should occur earlier in the day. If he is anxious before a particular business meeting, you may postpone the request to the next day, or preface your statement with, "I know now is not the time to ask you to listen to my questions, but after work tonight, can we spend ten minutes talking together?"

Besides employing the "I" statements and trying to be empathic, ask yourselves, "How else can we improve communication in our marriage?"

5. Sexual satisfaction can be maintained in spite of programed intercourse.

One of the questions I persistently ask of infertile couples is how has your sexual satisfaction changed? Although a private matter, most husbands and wives are straightforward and quick in their replies. "What satisfaction? Sex is for procreation, now it's a job...we always have a team of medical professionals, so to speak, in our bedroom."

In the main, a substantial proportion of infertile people begin to feel less sexual desire, less satisfaction, increased performance anxiety, in addition to feeling unattractive and even unlovable. Neither one of you is to blame for these feelings. They are common baggage on the trip through infertility and its treatment.

Sexual expression is meant to bring pleasure to our lives. Not only is there no pleasure, but in some cases sexual intercourse becomes an anxiety-laden event which the couple dreads. Countless numbers of couples use inter uterine insemination with the husband's sperm in which he masturbates in a specimen cup, an act some men begin to detest. Then the doctor injects the semen into the wife's uterus via a catheter. Sexual drive, in this instance, became a sarcastic joke, as Julie put it, "Dr. Smith is in the driver's seat, we are out of the car and out of control."

<u>Is there lovemaking after, or even during infertility treatments</u>? Definitely. Here are a few simple steps you can take to stoke the fire in your love life dampened by infertility. First, try to separate lovemaking from procreative sex by changing venues. Use the guest bedroom, for example, for renewed sexual bonding. Secondly, use the well known addition of massage oils, candles, or incense. If you are inclined, bring some party foods to the occasion, play music from the era in which you first met. Rent a movie, hold hands, pretend you are courting. Allow the sexual tension to build even to the point of postponing intercourse or orgasm on one occasion until you rendez-vous again. These and so many other changes can enliven the romance in your sexual expression.

6. Your families and friends are not the enemy.

It is important to constantly remind ourselves that our families and friends are experiencing grief and anxiety over our situation, also. Their comments and actions usually are well-meant, even though we cannot comprehend many times how they can respond to our crisis the way they do. If you and your spouse are arguing, don't bring "your mother" or "your best friend" into the fight. Remember, you are having enough of a problem dealing with this situation. Don't add the burden of others' actions and words.

<u>When we blend families and have stepchildren, we have even more challenges to meet</u>. Our attempts to bear children may become more stressful when we are coping with a disgruntled child from our spouse's previous marriage. The role of stepparent may involve an arduous struggle, we may feel unsuccessful at nurturing our stepchildren because they resent that we are not their biological parents. The unhappy stepchild may be a constant reminder of our own reproductive loss, make us feel more inadequate, our egos further deflated. Stepfamilies can and do work, however, even as new babies are born, but support groups and written resources are invaluable tools in paving the road to equanimity. Simple parenting techniques, especially regarding the major discipline role the biological parent should take, can rejuvenate faltering stepfamilies. The *Seven Steps To A Smoother Marriage* are

especially critical when you are living in a blended family. Keep these ideas in mind when you are interacting with your mate.

Our Thoughts and Feelings...

Seven Steps
To A Smoother Marriage.

**1. When you are together, modify your environ-
ment so that stress is minimal.**

Julie and Mark, arriving at home after work, usually
argued at dinner time about who would cook, who would
clean up, then the disagreement would escalate to chores,
and so on. Their solution was to designate which days one
would cook and the other clean up. Furthermore, they
decided to meditate for 10 minutes immediately upon
returning home so that they were in a calmer frame of
mind.

**2. Help each other release anger in constructive
ways.**

The most creative example I can share is the time Sandi
and Tim, after a negative pregnancy test, drove 20 minutes
out of town to a desolate country road, where Tim opened
the car doors and Sandi slammed them with all of her
might, occasionally yelling furiously as she ran around the
car. This beautiful picture illustrates how Tim not only
accepted his wife's voicing her anger, but assisted her in
expressing it. I like to use this example with couples when
explaining practical ways to help your mate express
feelings.

3. Be honest, but respect the feelings of your mate.

Use words that convey caring when you are suggesting a change in your spouse's behavior. Always leave an opening for your mate to change or redeem himself/herself. For instance, instead of saying, "The way you acted in front of the doctor humiliated me. I don't want you to go with me anymore." How about "I felt humiliated when you shook your finger at the doctor. Can we talk about other ways you and I could express our frustration?"

4. Avoid labeling your spouse or using disparaging generalizations.

Remarks such as, "You <u>really don't care about me</u>, you are just <u>obsessed</u> about having a baby," could be rephrased to, "I feel hurt when you avoid talking with me. I need to know that you still love me even if we can't have a baby right now."

5. Pay attention, not only to what is said, but also to the non-verbal expression.

When times are tense, repeat and validate your mate's statement to make certain you heard what you thought you heard. For example, "John, you told the doctor we could use donor sperm, but I sensed, by the way you held your head, that perhaps you weren't entirely comfortable with the idea, can we talk about it?" Or, in another discussion, you might ask, "Judy, you say you won't go to my mom's for dinner because she asks too many questions. Are there additional things that bother you about going there?"

6. Remember how soothing a gentle touch can be.

In some cases, touch is better than talk. If we are unsure of what words will accurately express our empathy, we can guide our mates to a comfortable spot and sit close or hold each other. When we attend to each other in this way, the more chances we have of expressing our true selves, not distracted by the chatter of the news on Wall Street or the neighbor's dog. Quiet, close moments together generate authenticity.

7. Above all else, listen to each other.

Someone very wise once said that we *hear* with our ears, but that we *listen* with our hearts and our souls. You are both grieving and you are each other's partners in your grief, just as you are partners in joy.

Be kind to each other and love each other unconditionally. You will get through this, if you make the journey together.

LISTEN

When I ask you to listen to me
and you start giving advice
you have not done what I asked.

When I ask you to listen to me
and you begin to tell me why I shouldn't feel that way,
you are trampling on my feelings.

When I ask you to listen to me
and you feel you have to do something to solve my problems,
you have failed me, strange as that may seem.

Listen! All I asked was that you listen
not talk or do – just hear me.
Advice is cheap. 35 ¢ will get you both Dear Abby
and Billy Graham in the same newspaper.
And I can do for myself; I'm not helpless.
Maybe discouraged and faltering, but not helpless.

When you do something for me that I can and need to do
for myself, you contribute to my fear and weakness.

But, when you accept as a simple fact that I do feel what I feel,
no matter how irrational, then I can quit trying to convince you
and can get about the business of understanding
what's behind this irrational feeling.
And when that's clear, the answers are obvious,
and I don't need advice.

Irrational feelings make sense
when we understand what's behind them.

Perhaps that's why prayer works, sometimes, for some people
because God is mute
and God doesn't give advice or try to fix things.
God just listens and lets you work it out for yourself.

So, please listen and just hear me.
And, if you want to talk,
wait a minute for your turn
and I'll listen to you.

Anonymous

102

I hope that this book has helped you gain a better understanding of how the problems related to infertility affect us all – as individuals and as a couple, as family and friends. It is just one of the situations we face that once again point out that life is not always fun and definitely not fair, but there are still choices. This is *not* a hopeless situation. If you really want a child, there can be a child (or children) in your lives. The decision you have to make is *how* those children will enter your life. If you have read the book, talked it over, and have discovered that your lives will be full and meaningful without children, that is the right choice for you. You need not apologize for it, or defend it.

My closing words in the last chapter were, "Be kind to each other and love each other unconditionally. You will get through this, if you don't make the journey alone, but together." Take these words to heart and also be kind to yourself and love yourself. Take care of yourself. Give yourself permission to express your feelings. Protect yourself and your feelings. Take pride in who you are and what you have accomplished. Take courage and have confidence in who you are.

Remember, no matter how many people "help" you through this situation, you <u>are</u> your own best counselor.

REFERENCES

NEW BOOKS ON INFERTILITY

Cooper, Susan L. & Glazer, Ellen S. **Beyond Infertility-The New Paths to Parenthood.** Lexington Books, 1994.

In this comprehensive text, the authors address state-of-the-art information on the emotional, medical, and legal aspects of infertility, with special emphasis on A.R.T. and third party reproduction, including surrogacy. Included is a glossary of technical terms used in infertility diagnosis and treatment.

Johnston, Patricia Irwin. **Taking Charge of Infertility.** Perspective Press, 1994.

This recent, extremely well-organized text on infertility, emphasizes how you can take control of every facet of treatment by taking concrete steps toward goals you and your partner choose. The book contains numerous practical lists for problem solving and it includes chapters on the complex issues of collaborative reproduction. Pertinent resources and reading material are described after every chapter.

GENERAL READING

Benson, Herbert and Klipper, Miriam Z. **The Relaxation Response**. Avon, 1975.

The authors' simple 10 minute technique is described in the section on meditation.

Covey, Stephen R. **The Seven Habits of Highly Effective People**. S&S Trade, 1989.

Covey's ideas are useful for infertile persons because of the emphasis on sorting out what you need to do for yourself. People in treatment for infertility may feel as though they are losing control of their lives. These ideas for gaining control can be beneficial.

Estes, Clarissa Pinkola. **Women Who Run With Wolves**. New York. Ballentine Books, 1992.

Dr. Estes renews our faith in the power of our instinctual natures. Her work, a compendium of folktales and traditional wisdom, may help renew your spiritual self.

Gold, Michael. **And Hannah Wept**. Philadelphia. JPS, 1988.

The author and his wife experienced infertility. He shares his philosophy about reproductive loss in the context of his religious beliefs.

Jeffers, Susan. **Feel the Fear and Do It Anyway**. New York. Harcourt Brace Jovanovich, 1987.

Not written for infertile people per se, the advice suits anyone, especially those whose self-confidence has been shaken by the vicissitudes of infertility.

Kushner, Harold. **When Bad Things Happen To Good People**. Schocken, 1989.

I consider Kushner's book a classic for helping us avoid self-blame, and embrace the goodness in people and in God.

Manning, Doug. **Don't Take My Grief Away**. New York. Harper & Row, 1979.

If you have no spiritual advisor, this author will assist you in accepting and honoring your grief. I have found all but the last chapters extremely helpful.

ADOPTION

Brodzinsky, David, Schecter, Marshall D. et al. **Being Adopted - The Lifelong Search for Self**. New York. Doubleday, 1992.

This book is the most helpful I've found for giving a positive but realistic representation of the adoption experience.

CHILD-FREE LIFESYTLES

Carter, Mike and Jean. **Sweet Grapes: How to Stop Being Infertile and Start Living Again.** Perspectives Press, 1989.

The authors trace their journey from infertility to unfertility and decide finally to enjoy a child-free lifestyle.

Notes

Notes

Notes

Notes

HOW TO BECOME YOUR OWN BEST INFERTILITY COUNSELOR

Order by Mail

Just mail your completed Order Form to:
JOLANCE Press, 259 Riverside Parkway
Ft. Thomas, KY 41075

Print or Type Shipping Address

Name_____

Organization_____

Title_____Phone_____

Address_____

City & State_____Zip_____

Method of Payment
Check or money order made payable to: JOLANCE Press
(no currency, please)

Institutional purchase order no._____

Tax exemption no._____

Quantity	Unit Price	Subtotal
	$8.95	$
	$3.00 Each, shipping & handling	+
	54¢ each, sales tax, **KY residents only**	+
	TOTAL Enclosed	$

If you have a friend who may be interested in this book, please write their name here and we'll send them some more information.

Name_____Phone_____

Address_____

City & State_____Zip_____

Terms & Conditions: All prices are effective March 15, 1995 and are subject to change without notice. All payments must be made in U.S. dollars. Shipping charges apply to orders within the 48 continental United States. Kentucky residents are required to pay Kentucky sales tax. Books will be shipped within three weeks of receipt of order.